Hello Kitty® Beads Activity Book

Hello Kitty & Her Friends Crafts Club

by Kris Hirschmann

Scholastic Inc.

New York Toronto London Auckland Sydney
Mexico City New Delhi Hong Kong Buenos Aires

Designer: Lee Kaplan
Illustrations: Yancey Labat
Photographs: Kayt Hester-Lent

ISBN: 0-439-32845-4

12 11 10 9 8 7 6 5 4 3 2 1   2 3 4 5 6/0

Printed in the U.S.A.
First Scholastic Printing, June 2002

Table of Contents

Beads Are Fun!

Hello Kitty just loves beads—their colors, their shapes, their sizes. And with so many choices, the project possibilities are "almost" endless! In this book, Hello Kitty shares with you 24 of her favorite bead crafts. One of her pals, Thomas, has come along to help out with the activities, too.

You can make these projects by yourself, or you can plan a get-together with your friends. Either way, what better way to spend hours of happy time!

Let's Get Started

With this book, you get five types of beads: regular pony beads, shimmery pony beads, clear round beads, mini beads, and letter beads. You also get elastic cord and a cute Hello Kitty box to organize and store everything.

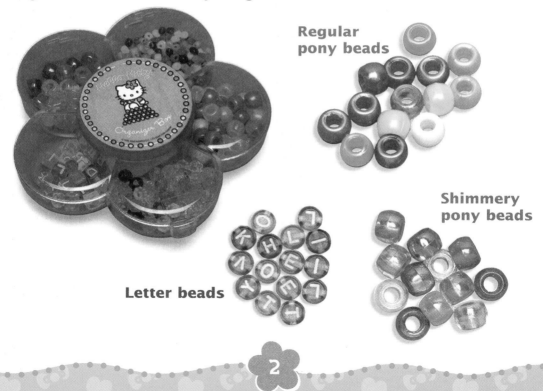

Regular pony beads

Shimmery pony beads

Letter beads

Whatever else you'll need for these crafts can be found around your house or at a craft store. Here's what you'll need:

- Ruler
- Scissors
- Large (1") safety pins
- Old T-shirt
- Pipe cleaner
- Hair clip
- Self-stick magnet sheet
- Glue
- Tape

- Colored paper
- Coffee straws
- Thread and string
- Twist ties
- Bobby pins
- Cardboard
- Toothpicks
- Paint
- Paintbrush
- Water

- Waxed paper
- Air-drying clay
- Food coloring
- Elbow macaroni
- Disposable cups
- Paper towel
- More beads or cord (if you run out)

Mini beads

Clear round beads

Bead It *with* Hello Kitty

Accessorizing can be a lot of fun—especially when you wear things you make yourself—from bracelets and bows, to necklaces and other jewelry!

Beaded Anklet:

Hello Kitty loves to make this anklet in colors that match her favorite outfits. (P.S. You can also wear this anklet as a bracelet.)

What You Do:

1. Cut a piece of elastic cord about 24" long. Fold the cord in half, and tie a very small loop in the folded end.

2. Tape the loop to a table so you can work more easily.

3. Feed a clear round bead (any color you want) onto both of the cord ends, as shown.

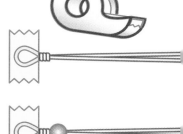

What You Need:

- **Scissors**
- **Elastic cord**
- **Ruler**
- **Tape**
- **Clear round beads** (any colors)
- **Mini beads** (any colors)

4. Feed each cord end through two different clear round beads in another color from the one you used in step 3.

5. Now, feed both string ends through a clear round bead of the same color you used in step 3.

6. Feed both string ends through two mini beads of any color.

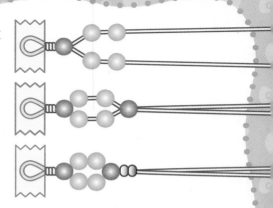

7. Repeat the pattern you made in steps 3 through 6 until the anklet is just the right size to go around your ankle.

8. When you're finished feeding on beads, tie the ends in a double knot around the loop, then trim off any loose ends.

HELLo KiTTY SAYS

Pink and purple are two of my favorite colors! What are yours?

Message Necklace:

Thomas makes a necklace that says "I Love Hello Kitty." You can, too!

What You Do:

1. Cut a piece of elastic cord about 20" long.

2. Arrange your letter beads in front of you so they spell "I Love Hello Kitty."

3. String the letter beads, in order, onto the elastic cord. As you string, put two mini beads between each word for a space, as shown.

4. Add whatever decorative beads you like to either side of your finished message.

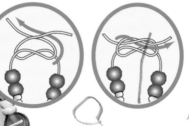

5. Use a double knot to tie the two string ends together, as shown in these pictures.

What You Need:

- Scissors
- Elastic cord
- Ruler
- Letter beads
- Mini beads
- Other beads of your choice

6. Trim the ends of the string and place your pretty necklace around your neck!

Beaded Bows:

Thomas is making a present for Hello Kitty. What would she like?
A bow, of course! You can make your own beaded bow to wear, too.

What You Do:

1. Poke the pipe cleaner through four pony beads of any color. Arrange the beads so they are in the middle of the pipe cleaner, then poke one end of the pipe cleaner back through the first bead, as shown, and pull tightly.

2. Feed a total of 22 pony beads onto each of the two ends of the pipe cleaner (11 beads on each side) of any color you want.

3. Loop each end of the pipe cleaner around to form two loops, and feed them back through the bottom bead, as shown. Pull the pipe cleaner tightly.

4. Bend the ends of the pipe cleaner around a hair clip to hold the bow in place. You can also glue the pipe cleaner ends onto the clip, if you want.

What You Need:

- **12" pipe cleaner (any color)**
- **26 regular pony beads (any colors)**
- **Hair clip**
- **Glue (optional)**

Daisy Chain Bracelet:

This pretty bracelet is just like a daisy chain, but it's even better because the flowers never fade!

What You Do:

1. Cut a piece of elastic cord about 18" long. Tape one end of the cord to a table so you can work more easily.

2. Tie a double knot about 1" in on the cord.

3. Feed the loose end of the cord through six mini beads of the same color—these will form the petals of your daisy. Bring the end of the cord back through the first bead to form a circle. Pull the cord tightly so the bead circle is snug against the double knot you tied in step 2.

4. Poke the cord through another mini bead of a different color (this will be the center of your daisy), then down through the fourth bead in the circle. (Look at the picture to see how to do this.) Pull the string tightly.

What You Need:

- Scissors
- Elastic cord
- Ruler
- Tape
- Mini beads (any colors)

5. Tie a double knot against the daisy to hold it together.

6. Repeat steps 2 through 5 to form more daisies until the bracelet is long enough to go around your wrist. Each time you repeat the steps, you should start about an inch below the previous daisy.

7. Tie the cord ends in a double knot, then trim any loose ends.

HELLO KITTY SAYS

I love daisies! They are so cheerful and pretty. What colors will your daisies be?

Beaded Hello Kitty Pin:

Pins are a fun way to display cool beaded designs. How would you like to wear a pin with Hello Kitty's initials?

What You Do:

1. Choose a picture to make from the patterns on page 42—Hello Kitty's initials, a butterfly, or a heart. Here, we're using Hello Kitty's initials.

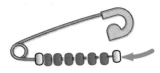

2. Put mini beads of the correct colors onto seven safety pins in the correct order, as in the pattern. Close each safety pin after you finish adding the beads.

3. Poke another safety pin through a small part of your shirt, as shown in the picture.

4. Slide the seven beaded pins onto the shirt pin. Make sure the beaded pins are in the right order and that the beaded side is facing out from the shirt.

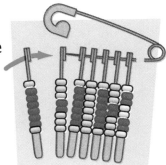

What You Need:

- **Mini beads (see pattern on page 42 for colors needed)**
- **9 large (1") safety pins**
- **Shirt you want to wear**

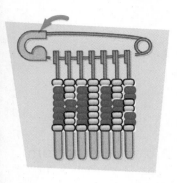

5. Poke the shirt pin through another small part of fabric, then close it.

6. Put the last safety pin through the bottom holes of the seven beaded pins to hold the ends together.

Butterfly

HK Initials

Heart

HELLo KiTTY SAYS

Can you figure out how to make a pin with your own initials?

Funky Fringe:

Hello Kitty and Thomas make a neat beaded fringe to turn an old T-shirt into an exciting work of art!

What You Do:

1. Cut 4" slits straight up from the bottom of an old T-shirt all the away around. The slits should be about $\frac{1}{2}$" apart. When you finish cutting the slits, you will have strips hanging down all the way around the bottom edge of your T-shirt.

2. Poke two of the strips through a pony bead. Push the bead up to the top of the strips.

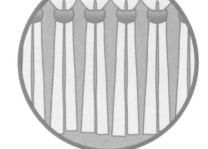

What You Need:

- Scissors
- Ruler
- Old T-shirt
- Regular pony beads (any colors)

3. Repeat step 2 all the way around the T-shirt.

4. Gather together a strip from one bead and a strip from the next bead. Poke them both through another pony bead. Push the bead up until it hangs just a little bit below the first row of beads.

5. Tie both strips in a knot to hold the beads in place.

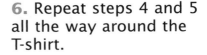

6. Repeat steps 4 and 5 all the way around the T-shirt.

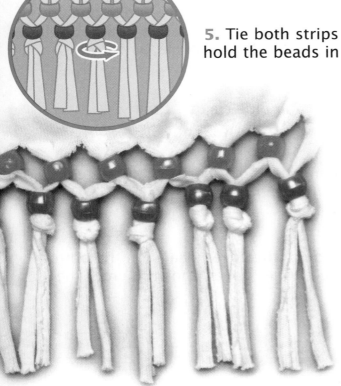

HELLO KITTY SAYS

I feel super-cool in my funky beaded shirt. I bet a beaded fringe would look great on Thomas's bandanna, too!

Princess Tiara:

A princess tiara looks pretty, and it's so Hello Kitty!

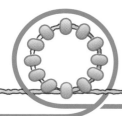

What You Do:

1. Feed a pipe cleaner through 12 of your shimmery pony beads of any color. Arrange the beads so they are in the middle of the pipe cleaner, then poke one end of the pipe cleaner back through the first bead to form a circle, as shown.

2. Pull the ends of the pipe cleaner tightly.

3. Feed three shimmery pony beads of a different color onto each end of the pipe cleaner.

4. Poke another pipe cleaner through the seven beads on the bottom row. Bend both ends of this pipe cleaner up, as shown. Center the pipe cleaner.

What You Need:

- **2 to 3 twelve-inch pipe cleaners (white or metallic)**
- **24 shimmery pony beads**
- **Bobby pins**

5. Feed three more beads onto each end of the bent pipe cleaners.

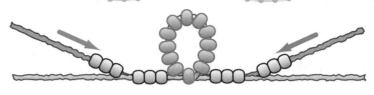

6. Wrap each end of the first pipe cleaner around the upper bead loop, as shown.

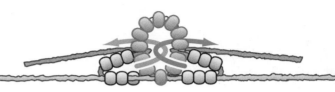

7. Bend the leftover ends of the first pipe cleaner down. Wrap them around the second pipe cleaner to hold them in place.

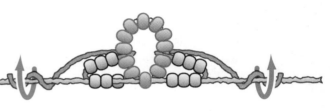

8. Bend the second pipe cleaner into a circle, and twist the ends to close the tiara. If the tiara is too small for you, twist an additional pipe cleaner to both ends to make it bigger.

9. Use some bobby pins to secure the tiara to your head.

HELLo KiTTY SAYS

When I wear my tiara, I'm Princess Hello Kitty!

Sparkly Ring:

Hello Kitty loves to sparkle and shine, so she made herself a bunch of these cute rings!

What You Do:

1. Cut a piece of elastic cord that is about 12" long.

2. String 15 to 20 mini beads of the same color onto the cord—just enough to wrap around your finger. Poke one end of the cord back through the first bead to form a circle.

3. String two clear round beads of the same color onto each end of the cord.

4. Poke each end of the cord back through the top mini bead to make a loop, as shown.

5. Arrange the ends of the cord so they pass through the loops, as shown. Pull tightly.

6. Tie the ends in a double knot. Trim off any excess cord.

What You Need:

- **Scissors**
- **Elastic cord**
- **Ruler**
- **15–20 mini beads (all same color)**
- **4 clear round beads (any colors)**

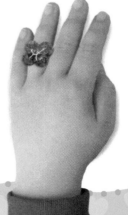

Fancy Feet:

Why wear plain shoelaces when you can dress them up with beads, as Hello Kitty does?

What You Do:

1. Take the shoelaces all the way out of a pair of shoes.

2. String three regular pony or clear round beads onto the shoelace. Arrange the beads so they are right in the middle of the shoelace.

3. Poke the shoelace ends through the top of the shoe, as shown, making sure the beads stay in the middle of the shoelace.

4. Lace up the rest of the shoe, adding pony or clear round beads as you go. You can use the picture to get ideas, or you can make up your own shoelace designs.

5. Repeat steps 2 through 4 with the other shoelace and shoe.

What You Need:

- **Any shoes with shoelaces**
- **Regular pony beads or clear round beads (any colors)**

HELLO KITTY SAYS

Now go strut your stuff!

"Beadazzled" at School

Hello Kitty decorates her locker, backpack, and more with beads. So can you!

Heart Bookmark:

You can make a bunch of these easy bookmarks in all different colors.

What You Do:

1. Hold three pipe cleaners so their ends are even. Twist the ends on one side together.

2. Braid the pipe cleaners for about 5" to 7". Look at the picture to see how to make a braid. You will have to bend each pipe cleaner slightly as you go.

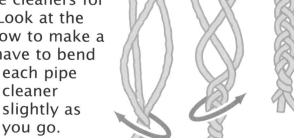

What You Need:

- **3 twelve-inch pipe cleaners (any colors)**
- **Ruler**
- **14 regular pony beads (any colors)**
- **Scissors**

18

3. Squeeze two of the pipe cleaner ends together, and feed them through seven of your pony beads. Then poke the third pipe cleaner end through another seven beads. You will now have two beaded ends.

4. Bend both of the beaded ends inward to make a heart shape.

5. Twist the ends together to close the heart.

6. Trim any excess pipe cleaner.

HELLO KITTY SAYS

These bookmarks are so easy to make, and they make great gifts, too.

Magnetic Locker Ants:

Thomas made these magnetic ants and put them on Hello Kitty's locker just for fun.

What You Do:

1. Press three pony beads onto the sticky side of a self-stick magnet sheet, as shown. Put little dabs of glue between and under the beads.

2. When the glue is dry, cut the magnet sheet around the beads.

3. Snip three 1½" pieces of pipe cleaner. Stick each piece through each of the three pony beads. Make sure each bead is centered on the pipe cleaner.

4. Squeeze a dab of glue into each bead to hold the pipe cleaners in place.

5. Use the tip of a toothpick to put two tiny dots of paint on your ant's head. These will be the eyes.

6. After the glue and paint dry, take your magnetic ant to school, and stick it to your locker for some extra décor!

What You Need:

- **3 regular pony beads (any colors)**
- **Self-stick magnet sheet**
- **Glue**
- **Scissors**
- **Pipe cleaner (any color)**
- **Ruler**
- **Toothpick**
- **Paint**

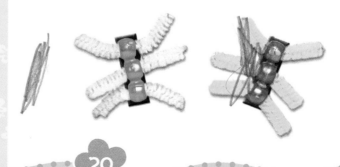

Measuring with Beads:

Pony beads are exactly ¼" wide. So Hello Kitty decided to make her own beaded ruler to jazz up her school supplies. You can, too!

1 inch

What You Do:

1. Arrange two pipe cleaners so their ends are even. Twist the stems together about 1" from one end.

2. Feed both pipe cleaners through the 36 pony beads. Arrange the colors in groups of four, as shown.

3. After you finish adding all the beads, twist the other end of the pipe cleaners together to hold the beads tightly in place.

4. Bend the stems on both ends of the ruler into heart shapes like the ones here.

5. Each group of four beads is exactly 1" long. Use a fine-tip permanent marker to mark the inches on your ruler.

What You Need:

- **2 twelve-inch pipe cleaners (any colors)**
- **Ruler**
- **36 regular pony beads (any colors)**
- **Fine-tip permanent marker**

21

HELLo KiTTY SAYS

You can use your cool bead ruler to measure anything...except the size of your friendship!

Super Zipper Pull:

Zipper pulls are a fun way to dress up backpacks and gym bags!

What You Do:

1. Cut three pieces of elastic cord about 10" long each.

2. Hold the three pieces so their ends are even. Then, feed them through the hole in a zipper pull or safety pin. Arrange the pieces so they hang evenly on either side of the zipper pull.

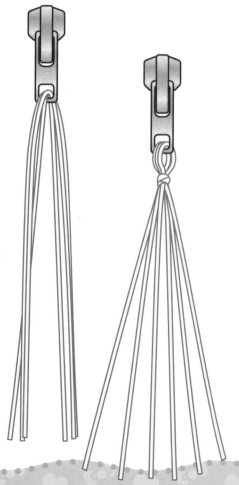

3. Tie all of the pieces in one big knot near the zipper pull. Pull tightly.

What You Need:

- Scissors
- Elastic cord
- Ruler
- Backpack or gym bag with a zipper pull
- Safety pin (optional)
- 44 mini beads (any colors)
- 11 pony beads (any colors)

4. Poke all of the ends through one mini bead, then through eleven pony beads, then through another mini bead.

5. Poke one end of the cord through seven mini beads. Tie a double knot at the end to hold the beads in place, and trim off any excess cord.

6. Repeat step 5 with the five remaining ends.

23

HELLO KITTY SAYS
I made a zipper pull in my school colors. What colors will you choose?

Bead Bonanza

There's no end to how creative you can be with beads!

Made in the Shade:

Hello Kitty loves to add beads to sunglasses to give them a cute new look.

What You Do:

1. Set an old pair of sunglasses on a table. Prop them up if necessary so the lenses sit flat.

2. Squeeze a thin line of glue along any of the parts of the sunglass frame.

3. Carefully set any beads you like on the glue. You can use tweezers to make it easier to place the beads, if you want.

4. When you're done placing beads, let the glue dry completely. Then wear your way-cool sunglasses anywhere you like!

What You Need:

- **Pair of sunglasses**
- **Glue**
- **Beads (any types, any colors)**
- **Tweezers (optional)**

24

Thomas's Roller Skates:

Thomas roller skates wherever he goes. You can make your own roller skates that are just like his!

What You Do:

1. Cut two shoe shapes from cardboard using the pattern on page 42. Have a grown-up poke a small hole in the top of each shape, using a pin.

2. Put four dabs of glue on the bottom of each shoe shape, as shown. Put a pony bead on each dab of glue to make the wheels. Let the glue dry.

3. Cut four thin strips of colored paper. Each strip should be about 1" long.

4. Use glue to attach two of the strips to each roller skate.

5. Cut a piece of string about 8" long. Fold it in half, and tie a loop in it. Poke the ends of the string through the holes in the roller skates, and double knot them. Now hang them wherever you like!

What You Need:

- Scissors
- Colorful cardboard
- Pin
- Glue
- 8 regular pony beads
- Colored paper
- Ruler
- String

Beady Buddies:

If you arrange beads just right, they can make fun pictures and shapes.

What You Do:

1. Cut a piece of cord about 48" long. Fold it in half, and tie a loop in the folded end. Tape the loop to a table so you can work more easily.

2. Decide which beady buddy you want to make —Hello Kitty or the salamander—by choosing from the two patterns on pages 42–43. We decided to make Hello Kitty. Whichever you choose, lay your pony beads out in the correct order, based upon the pattern.

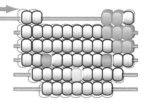

3. Feed coffee straws through some of the bead rows to hold them in place. If you're making Hello Kitty, place a coffee straw through each of the rows.✳ Trim all the coffee straws so they just fit inside the beads.

✳ If you're making the salamander, place a coffee straw through all the rows of its body—but not its feet.

What You Need:

- Scissors
- Elastic cord
- Ruler
- Tape
- Regular pony beads
- Coffee straws
- Two twist ties (optional)
- String (optional)

4. Follow the diagram to weave the cord back and forth through the coffee straws that are inside the beads.

5. When you get to the bottom of the design, tie the ends of the cord in a double knot. Pull tightly. Then trim off any excess cord.

6. If you're making Hello Kitty, you can add two twist ties for her whiskers. Twist them a couple of times in the middle to connect them. Then slide the ties through the row of beads that has Hello Kitty's eyes so that a little bit of the twist ties sticks out on each side. Bend the ends of the twist-tie whiskers up and down.

7. Now you can tie a string around your beady buddy and use it in a necklace or hang it up for decoration.

Super Sun Catcher:

Rise and shine, Hello Kitty, and catch the sun's light.

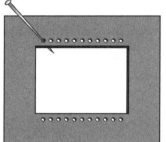

What You Do:

1. Cut a piece of cardboard 4½" high and 5" wide. Ask a grown-up to cut out the opening in the center (based on the size of the pattern on page 43) and to punch 11 small holes in the top and bottom of the frame, as shown in the same pattern. This will be your Hello Kitty sun catcher frame.

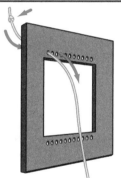

2. Cut a piece of cord about 40" long.

3. Poke one end of the cord through the first hole from back to front. Tie a double knot in the back of the frame.

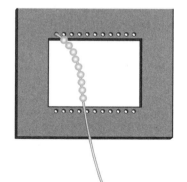

4. Look at the pattern on page 43 to see which colors of beads are in the first row of your Hello Kitty sun catcher. String those beads in order onto the cord.

What You Need:

- Scissors
- Cardboard
- Ruler
- Pin
- Elastic cord
- Clear beads (see the pattern on page 43 for colors)

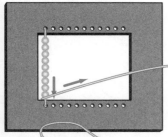

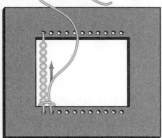

5. Poke the end of the cord through the hole at the bottom of the row. Loop it around and through the next hole, as shown. Pull tightly.

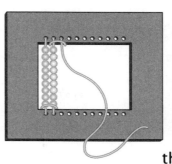

6. String the next row of beads onto the cord, following the pattern. Then poke the cord through the top hole, and loop it around and through the next hole the way you did in step 5.

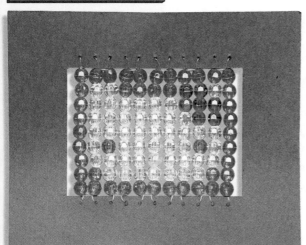

7. Continue adding rows and looping until your Hello Kitty sun catcher

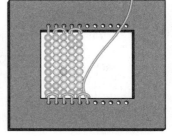

is complete. Tie a double knot to hold everything in place, then trim off any excess cord from the back.

HELLO KITTY SAYS

Put my picture in a place with plenty of sunlight. Then watch me shine!

Itty-bitty Snowman:

Hello Kitty loves making beaded mini snow people, winter or not.

What You Do:

1. Cut a small square of blue paper. Put a blob of glue in the middle of the square.

2. Lay a white pony bead flat on the glue, as shown. Glue two additional white pony beads on top of the first bead.

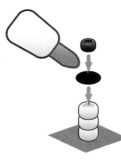

3. Cut a small circle of black paper, just an itty-bit bigger than a pony bead. Glue it to the top of your stack of white pony beads.

4. Glue the mini black bead to the top of the black paper (use tweezers if necessary). Let the glue dry completely.

What You Need:

- **Scissors**
- **Blue and black paper**
- **Glue**
- **3 white pony beads**
- **1 mini black bead**
- **Tweezers (optional)**
- **Black permanent marker**
- **Orange marker**

5. Then, use a permanent marker to draw eyes, a mouth, and buttons on your snowman. Use an orange marker to make the nose.

Sparkling Snowflake:

Hello Kitty and Thomas love the snow so much that sometimes they make their own bead snowflakes and hang them up.

What You Do:

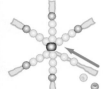

1. Cut a pipe cleaner into three equal pieces (about 4" long each). Hold the pieces so their ends are even, then poke all three pieces through a pony bead. Arrange the pony bead so it's in the middle of the pieces.

2. Bend the pipe cleaner pieces out so they form a six-pointed shape—like the shape of a star.

3. Feed four clear round beads onto each of the six pipe cleaner snowflake sides. Use any colors you like.

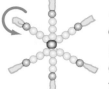

4. Bend the top of each pipe cleaner piece. Tuck the end inside the top bead.

5. To make a loop to hang your star, cut a small piece of string, and feed it through one of the pieces of pipe cleaner that you just bent. Tie a double knot and trim off any excess string.

What You Need:

- Scissors
- 12" pipe cleaner (any color)
- Ruler
- 1 regular pony bead (any color)
- 24 clear round beads (any colors)
- String

Magic Wand:

Abracadabra! **Hello Kitty adores magic shows. Here's how to magically make her magic wand.**

What You Do:

1. Poke the pipe cleaner through all 25 beads, in the order shown in the picture. Arrange the row of beads so it's centered on the pipe cleaner.

2. Bend the pipe cleaner in half, keeping the center pony bead in the middle.

3. Carefully bend the rest of the pipe cleaner so it forms a star shape, as shown. Twist the pipe cleaner ends together where the beads meet.

What You Need:

- **1 twelve-inch pipe cleaner (any color)**
- **5 regular pony beads (any colors)**
- **20 clear round beads (any colors)**
- **Scissors**
- **Ribbon**
- **Ruler**
- **Glue**
- **Drinking straw**

4. Cut several pieces of ribbon about 18" long each. You can cut as many ribbon strips as you like.

5. Hold all of the ribbon strips so their ends are even. Then tie them around the pipe cleaner ends. Pull tightly and push the knot up until it's right at the base of the bead star.

6. Squeeze a few drops of glue into the drinking straw.

7. Poke the pipe cleaner ends into the drinking straw and push the straw up toward the star. Let the glue dry.

HELLO KITTY SAYS

Hocus pocus. I'm a magic kitty!

Itsy-bitsy Beady Flowers:

Once you get started making these cute little flowers, you'll want to make a whole bouquet, just like Hello Kitty does.

What You Do:

1. Cut a piece of elastic cord about 12" long.

2. Poke the cord through 14 mini beads—these will be the petals of your flower. Arrange the beads so they are in the middle of the cord.

3. Poke the cord ends back through the two middle beads, as pictured. Pull tightly.

4. Poke the cord ends in opposite directions through one bead of a different color—this will be the center of your flower. Pull tightly.

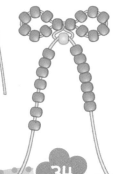

5. Poke each cord end through seven more beads of the same color you used in step 2.

What You Need:

- Scissors
- Elastic cord
- Ruler
- 35 mini beads
  (28 in any colors for
  your petals, 1 for
  your flower center,
  and 6 for your stem)

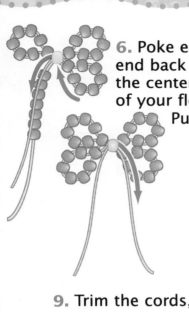

6. Poke each cord end back through the center bead of your flower. Pull tightly.

7. Poke both cord ends through six beads of a new color to make the stem of your flower.

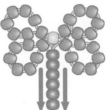

8. Tie a double knot at the bottom of the stem.

9. Trim the cords, as shown in the picture.

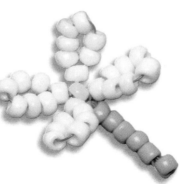

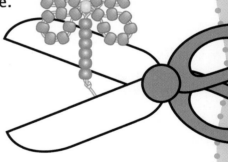

HELLO KITTY SAYS

These itsy-bitsy flowers are a bit tricky to make, but once you get the hang of it, you can do it!

Make Your Own Beads

It's fun to create with ready-made beads. But it can be just as fun to make crafts with beads you make yourself! Hello Kitty shows you how to make three kinds of beads that you can use for all kinds of projects.

Easy Paper Roll-ups:

You can make these pretty beads out of any kind of paper. Try colored paper, wrapping paper, and even magazine pictures.

What You Do:

1. Cut long, thin triangles out of your colored paper. Each triangle should be about 1" wide and 8" to 9" long. You need twenty triangles to make the necklace shown here.

2. Bend the wide end of one of the paper triangles over a toothpick.

3. Carefully spin the toothpick to roll up the triangle. Adjust the paper as you go to keep the roll centered.

What You Need:

- Scissors
- Colored paper, wrapping paper, or any other kind of colorful paper
- Ruler
- Toothpick
- Glue
- Elastic cord
- Pony beads (optional)

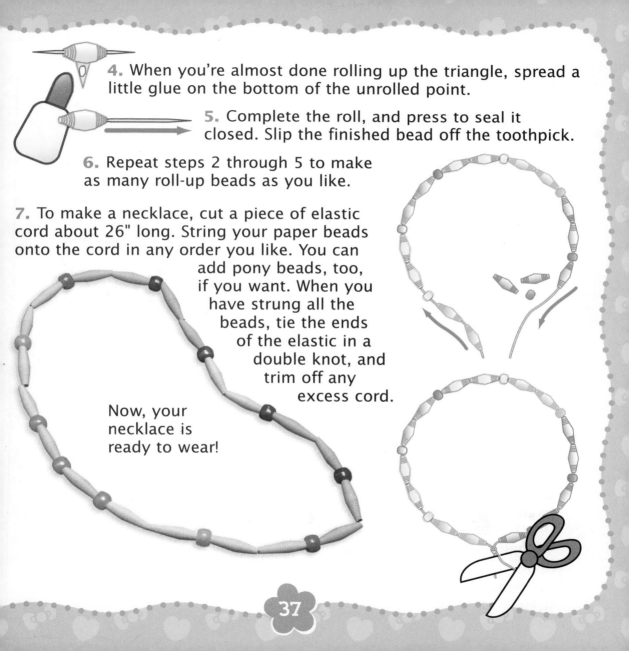

4. When you're almost done rolling up the triangle, spread a little glue on the bottom of the unrolled point.

5. Complete the roll, and press to seal it closed. Slip the finished bead off the toothpick.

6. Repeat steps 2 through 5 to make as many roll-up beads as you like.

7. To make a necklace, cut a piece of elastic cord about 26" long. String your paper beads onto the cord in any order you like. You can add pony beads, too, if you want. When you have strung all the beads, tie the ends of the elastic in a double knot, and trim off any excess cord.

Now, your necklace is ready to wear!

Cool Clay Charms:

You can make great beads out of clay. Clay is a fun and easy way to make lots of cool bead shapes!

What You Do:

1. Lay a piece of waxed paper on a table. Press a piece of clay into a flat slab on top of the waxed paper.

2. Use a toothpick to carve out any shape you like. You can use the patterns on page 43 as a guide, or you can make up your own shapes.

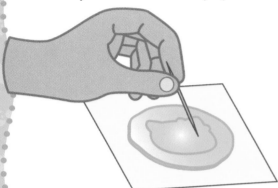

What You Need:

- Waxed paper
- Air-drying clay (available at any craft store)
- Toothpick
- Paint
- Paintbrush
- String

3. Use a toothpick to poke a hole through the top of your shape so you can feed a string through it when it's dry.

4. Set the finished shape aside (still on the waxed paper), and let it dry. (See the instructions on your clay package to see how long this will take.)

5. When the shape is completely dry, paint it however you like. Let the paint dry.

6. You can hang your clay charm bead from a necklace, a key chain, a zipper pull, or anything else that suits your fancy, by tying on a loop of string.

HELLO KITTY SAYS

I just love the charm that looks like my friend Thomas. Now I can take Thomas with me wherever I go!

Macaroni Twist Bracelet:

Macaroni makes great beads! Hello Kitty uses elbow macaroni or any kind of pasta that has a hole in it.

What You Do:

1. Set several disposable cups on a table. Into each cup, put a few drops of food coloring plus about two to three tablespoons of water. Make a different color of liquid in each cup.

2. Drop as many pieces of macaroni as you like into each cup. Let the macaroni pieces soak for about two minutes, then use tweezers to remove them from the liquid. Set the pasta on a paper towel, and let them dry completely (about an hour).

What You Need:

- **Disposable cups**
- **Food coloring**
- **Measuring spoon**
- **Water**
- **Uncooked macaroni (any kind of pasta with holes)**
- **Tweezers**
- **Paper towel**
- **Scissors**
- **Elastic cord**
- **Ruler**

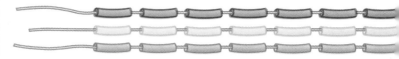

3. Cut three pieces of elastic cord about 12" long each.

4. Poke each of the three cords through as many macaroni pieces as you like. The macaroni on each string should be about 7" long.

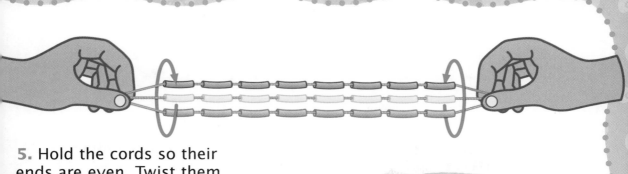

5. Hold the cords so their ends are even. Twist them so the macaroni winds into a spiral shape.

6. Use a double knot to tie all the cord ends together. Pull tightly. Trim the ends.

HELLo KiTTY SAYS

I love this craft. The jewelry pasta-bilities are endless!

Hello Kitty Patterns

Pattern for Beaded Hello Kitty Pin, pages 10–11

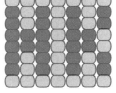

HK Initials Pattern

Butterfly Pattern

Heart Pattern

Pattern for Thomas's Roller Skates, page 25

Hello Kitty pattern for Beady Buddies, pages 26–27

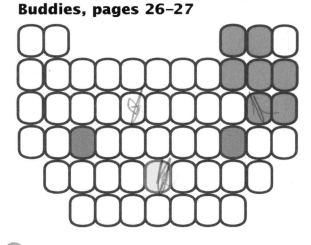

Salamander pattern for Beady Buddies, pages 26–27

Pattern for Super Sun Catcher, pages 28–29

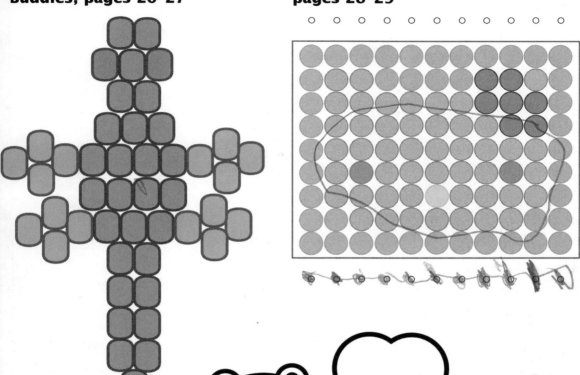

Patterns for Cool Clay Charms, pages 38–39

A Big Bead Good-bye from Hello Kitty

Beads are the best, aren't they? There are so many fun projects you can make with them. There's lots and lots of jewelry, of course (always a Hello Kitty favorite!), plus plenty of designs to add a Hello Kitty touch to your clothes.

Beads can also be used to decorate your room, add a little sparkle to your belongings, and spruce up your school accessories. What other fun things can you think of to do with beads?

Love,

xoxox Hello Kitty
(and Thomas too!)